THE BEST OF

THE BEST OF FRED BASSET

Summersdale Publishers Ltd
46 West Street
Chichester
West Sussex
PO19 1RP
UK

www.summersdale.com

Printed and bound in the China

ISBN: 978-1-84953-809-1

Substantial discounts on bulk quantities of Summersdale books are available to corporations, professional associations and other organisations. For details contact Nicky Douglas by telephone: +44 (0) 1243 756902, fax: +44 (0) 1243 786300 or email: nicky@summersdale.com.

FOREWORD

My father, Alex Graham, was often asked why he chose a basset hound to be the central character in his new cartoon strip. His response was that he often used dogs in cartoons for *Punch* and other periodicals. He had noticed the basset's unique shape and expressive features. By the early sixties, bassets were becoming fashionable, and celebrities, including Clint Eastwood, Marilyn Monroe and Rex Harrison, were acquiring them as pets. So, when he was invited to create a new family strip cartoon, the basset hound provided the perfect character.

In the first week of July, 1963, the headline news in the *Daily Mail* was all about espionage. Kim Philby and Stephen Ward were under investigation, while in the United States two couples had been arrested for a conspiracy to spy for Russia. However, for my dad and the Graham family, the excitement lay in the small notices at the bottom of the front page of the *Daily Mail* on Wednesday July 3rd, and then for the following two days.

The weekend was almost unbearable with anticipation. However, Fred Basset failed to appear in the Monday edition. I don't know why this happened. Perhaps a reader may know the answer? It was the next day, July 9th, that Fred appeared in the newspaper, growling, 'Aw hell, it's only a cat.' Certainly the strip made a strange bedfellow to Carol Day, Rip Kirby, Flook and Col. Pewter, all of which appeared above Fred in the cartoon section.

HERE'S FRED

Full name : Fred Basset, Esq.
Address : Page 10

Curiously, history repeated itself 50 years later. A charming and sympathetic article was prepared to celebrate Fred's half-century. It did not appear on July 9th but made it the following day. This time the explanation for the delayed appearance was totally understandable: Great Britain had a new tennis hero, Andy Murray, who had just won the men's singles at Wimbledon.

In compiling this book, I have included a section on music. It is already well documented that dad devoted his working life to cartoons. What is less well known is that he was a fine musician. Serving with the Argyll and Sutherland Highlanders during World War Two, he was a piper. We still have his kilt, bonnet and chanter. Throughout his life, he enjoyed playing the piano, the mandolin and any other instrument he could lay his hands on.

It is now many years since the Sunday strips have made an appearance in book form. I have included examples in the chapter entitled 'A Week in the Life of Fred'. I should explain that although these strips appear in the Sunday edition, they are of a general nature, albeit on occasion with a nod to Sunday activities. The Sunday strip is first published in the United States, where it is coloured and edited to suit the American audience. On its return to the United Kingdom, it reverts to its original format.

Fred Basset continues to enjoy worldwide syndication. At present, the furthest place of publication is Hobart, Tasmania. The strip is also translated into several different foreign languages, where poor old Fred acquires a different name each time. For example, in Germany Fred becomes Wurzel, where he is much enjoyed for his gentle humour. At the end of this book I have included an example of Fred in translation, which I hope will amuse.

It has been a pleasure revisiting Fred's adventures. I have to confess that making this selection has not been easy. You will no doubt notice that my choices are drawn primarily from the work that I have produced alongside Michael Martin, our talented artist. I apologise if this seems a little biased. Michael and I have tried to remain faithful to Dad's gentle humour and wry view of life. It is often said that you can't please everybody all of the time, but I hope that you, the reader, will find something to chuckle and smile about in this book.

Arran Graham

ACKNOWLEDGEMENTS

A big thank you to everyone who has helped in the creation of this book. In particular, I should like to show my gratitude to William Gardiner, our syndication agent and good friend; to Mo McFarland at Solo Syndication, who gave up her time to research the archives of Associated Newspapers and unearthed some hitherto unknown material; and to Dirk Handera of Bulls Press in Germany.

Finally, I am indebted to everyone at Summersdale for making this book possible. A special word of thanks goes to Madeleine, Anna and Claire for their advice, enthusiasm and love in bringing this project to fruition.

HOME COMFORTS

THE BEST OF FRED BASSET

BATH TIME

FRIENDS AND FOES

THE GAMES PEOPLE PLAY!

THE BEST OF FRED BASSET

MUSIC

THE BEST OF FRED BASSET

THE POST

ME, ME, ME...

GARDENING

COUNTRY PURSUITS

THE BEST OF FRED BASSET

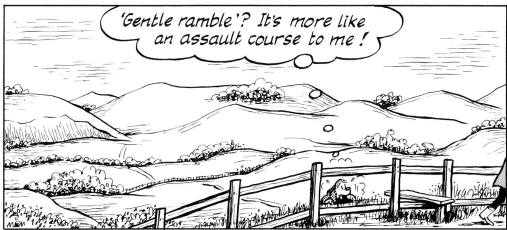

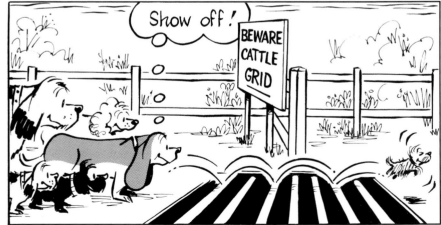

GOLF

Lemon sweater, pink shirt, orange and green check trousers and a matching cap!

It seems that when playing golf, anything goes!

THE BEST OF FRED BASSET

DOWN THE PUB

DREAM ON...

CHURCH AFFAIRS

LAW AND DISORDER

THE BEST OF FRED BASSET

MODERN TIMES

THE BEST OF FRED BASSET

A WEEK IN THE LIFE OF FRED

ON HOLIDAY

HOW LONG DO YOU THINK IT WILL TAKE, DEAR?

MMM... A COUPLE OF HOURS AT LEAST!

Desperate times call for desperate measures—

I spy with my little eye...

CHRISTMAS

FOREIGN PARTS

Have you enjoyed this book?
If so, why not write a review on your favourite website?

If you're interested in finding out more about our books,
find us on Facebook at **Summersdale Publishers**
and follow us on Twitter at **@Summersdale**.

Thanks very much for buying this Summersdale book.

www.summersdale.com

THE BEST OF
Fred Basset